THE NEW SWEDEN COLONY

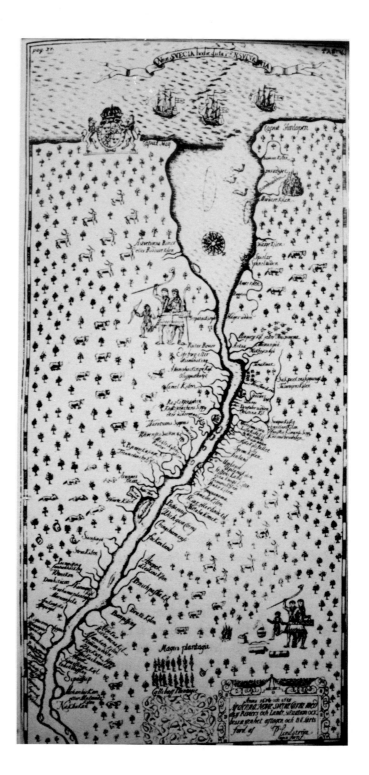

Map of the New Sweden colony in the
Delaware Valley drawn by Per Lindestrom,
ca. 1655
Courtesy of the Riksarkivet, Stockholm

THE NEW SWEDEN COLONY

February 6-May 15, 1988

NEW JERSEY STATE MUSEUM TRENTON, NEW JERSEY 1988
NEW JERSEY DEPARTMENT OF STATE

Partially funded by the New Sweden Commemorative Commission of New Jersey, the government of Sweden, the Swedish National Committee for New Sweden '88, the New Jersey Committee for the Humanities and the Pennsylvania Humanities Council with cosponsorship from the Pennsylvania State Museum and the New Jersey Historical Commission

Library of Congress Catalogue Card Number 88-620581
ISBN 0-938766-07-4

Edited by Lorraine E. Williams
Designed by John Crank & Associates,Inc.
Photographs by Tony Masso, Courtesy of Lending Institutions
Typeset and produced by the New Jersey State Museum
Printed by White Eagle Printing Co., Inc.

Cover: Detail of New Sweden colonists trading with the Indians from Thomas Campanius Holm *Description of New Sweden*,1702, published in Stockholm.

CONTENTS

7   FOREWORD
Leah P. Sloshberg

9   ACKNOWLEDGEMENTS
Lorraine E. Williams

11   INTRODUCTION

15   CHRONOLOGY

19   THE NEW SWEDEN COLONY
Catalogue of Exhibition

69   BIBLIOGRAPHY

FOREWORD

Leah P. Sloshberg
Director

The New Jersey State Museum is pleased to participate in the commemorative celebration of the 350th anniversary of the founding of the New Sweden Colony in the Delaware Valley. The presentation of this exhibition documents and visualizes this brief but very influential part of our regional and state history; brief, in that the actual life of the colony was only seventeen years, but influential in its many cultural contributions such as place names, music and religious traditions, architectural influences, and foodways that are still strong and vibrant.

In the development of the exhibition, the Museum staff has had the pleasure of working with the New Jersey Swedish community, with a national academic community having special interest in Swedish American cultural history, and with cultural, academic, and governmental organizations in Sweden. We appreciate the assistance and guidance of these legions. We are especially grateful to our funders: The New Sweden Commemorative Commission of New Jersey, the government of Sweden, the Swedish National Committee for New Sweden '88, the New Jersey Committee for the Humanities and the Pennsylvania Humanities Council. Without their financial support and the loans from the many institutions who have entrusted us with their treasures, this exhibition would not have been possible. Our appreciation and gratitude to all of you.

ACKNOWLEDGEMENTS

Lorraine E. Williams
Curator of Archaeology/Ethnology

The record of the New Sweden Colony presented in this exhibition is the outcome of three years of cooperation among scholars on both sides of the Atlantic Ocean. We have benefited from the generous sharing of expertise by the staff of our cosponsors and lending museums. Barry Kent and Stephen Warfel of the State Museum of Pennsylvania shared their detailed knowledge of the Susquehannock Indians. Richard Waldron of the New Jersey Historical Commission researched the history of the colony both in Sweden and in the Delaware Valley and helped locate documents and objects.

The exhibition would not have been possible without the unstinting cooperation of Swedish museums. The support of director Sune Zachrisson and curators Elizabeth Hidemark, Ingrid Bergman and Jonas Berg at the Nordiska Museet in Stockholm enabled us to present a comprehensive visual record of the New Sweden Colony which would otherwise have been impossible. Elizabeth Hidemark provided untiring support and contributed throughout the exhibition's development.

Special appreciation is owed to Bo Karlson of the Jonkoping Lans Museum for his research on Johan Printz and the loan of associated objects and graphic material.

We are extremely grateful to Arne Losman, director of Skoklosters Slott, Balsta, and Ulla Wagner, director, and Staffan Brunius, Curator of the Americas, at the Etnografiska Museet, Stockholm, for their generosity in loaning us Middle Atlantic Indian objects from their collections. These fragile objects, fashioned from organic materials, provide us with a rare opportunity to see 17th-century artifacts that have not survived in North America.

We would like to express our appreciation for the assistance of Jon Lindroth of the Riksarkivet, Pontus Grate of the Nationalmuseum and Bjore Westlund of the Kungliga Biblioteket in Stockholm.

On this side of the Atlantic we are grateful for the assistance of Paul Needham and David Wright of the J. Pierpont Morgan Library; Caterina Cherny and Zoriana Siokalo of the American Swedish Historical Museum; Roger Allen of the Philadelphia Maritime Museum; Donald Winer of the State Museum of Pennsylvania; Stephen Ferguson of Firestone Library, Princeton University; and Ruth Simmons of Special Collections and Archives, Rutgers University Libraries. William Sturtevant, Richard Hulan, Peter Wacker, Charles Gehring, and Marshall Becker shared the results of their many years of work on Indians and Europeans of the middle Atlantic area. Thorsten Karlsson, president of the Scandinavian American Heritage Society of New Jersey and the New Sweden Company, Inc., John Jacobson, assistant to the Secretary of State, and Beth Linnerson-Daly, program director of the New Sweden Commemorative Commission of New Jersey, helped throughout our work.

Such a complex project would have been impossible without the continuing support of Secretary of State Jane Burgio, Assistant Secretary of State Alvin Felzenberg, and State Museum Director Leah Sloshberg. Magnus Faxen, Consul General of Sweden has also provided unwavering support. Lars Georgson of the Swedish Consulate in New York, and Gunnel Myhrberg of the Swedish Information Service Office in New York have assisted in countless ways. First Ulf Lundin and then Beate Sydhoff as Cultural Counselor for the Embassy of Sweden supported the project in Sweden and here in the States. In Sweden, Anders Clasom and Birgitta Lonnell of the Swedish Institute have provided vital coordination between two continents.

The staff of the New Jersey State Museum responded admirably to the challenges of an international exhibition. The Archaeology Bureau staff, Karen Flinn, Gina Giambrone, Fran Mollett, and Marcia Sternberg coped wonderfully with the extra work entailed with international shipments, catalogue entries from two continents for text and label copy in the exhibition and catalogue, and development of educational programming for school classes. Karen Cummins, Suzanne Crilley and Susan Finkel developed adult educational programming to enhance visitors' enjoyment of the exhibition. The staff of the Exhibits Bureau worked creatively and tirelessly to install the exhibition according to the creative design prepared by John Crank Associates.

Finally, it is appropriate that the New Sweden Colony exhibition be a joint Swedish and American contribution to the celebration of the 350th anniversary of the beginning of New Sweden in the Delaware Valley. The Swedish National Committee for New Sweden '88 and the New Sweden Commemorative Commission of New Jersey have provided funding to make the exhibition a reality. Grants from the New Jersey Committee for the Humanities and the Pennsylvania Humanities Council have supported research for the exhibition.

INTRODUCTION

The 17th century was an age of discovery and expansion—in the arts, science, industry, and global exploration. European countries tried to spread their commercial and political influence throughout the world. Inspired by the riches that Spain and Portugal gained through their overseas colonies, Sweden, England and the Netherlands competed for control of the middle Atlantic seaboard of North America throughout the first half of the century.

While we generally think of the English and the Dutch as 17th-century colonial powers, we do not associate Sweden with early European colonialism. Yet from 1620 to 1720, Sweden was a European Great Power. Her continental possessions made of the Baltic Sea a Swedish lake. Finland was then a part of Sweden. At various times, so were portions of modern Poland, Latvia, Estonia, Lithuania, Germany, and the Soviet Union. By mid-century, the Swedes controlled trade in the Baltic and were one of the major military and political combatants in Germany during the Thirty Years' War (1618-1648).

But Sweden lacked the money and manpower to maintain her military and economic position in Europe, especially since she was at war throughout most of the 17th century. By the 1630s the English and the Dutch were beginning to realize profits from their colonial and commerical ventures, and such examples probably led the Swedes to found New Sweden.

In 1637, Swedish, Dutch and German stockholders formed the New Sweden Company to trade for furs and tobacco in North America. Under the command of Peter Minuit, the company's first expedition sailed from Sweden late in 1637 in two ships, *Kalmar Nyckel* and *Fogel Grip*. Minuit had been the governor of the Dutch colony, New Netherland, centered on Manhattan Island, from 1626 to 1631. The ships reached Delaware Bay in March 1638, and the settlers began to build a fort at the site of modern Wilmington, Delaware. They named it Fort Christina, after Sweden's twelve-year-old queen. It was the first permanent European settlement in the Delaware Valley.

In time, the colony consisted of farms and small settlements scattered along both banks of the Delaware River into modern Delaware, New Jersey and Pennsylvania. In the next seventeen years, eleven Swedish expeditions followed the first one, each bringing supplies and small numbers of Swedish and Finnish settlers.

New Sweden rose to its greatest heights during the governorship of Johan Printz (1643-1653). He extended settlement northward from Fort Christina along both sides of the Delaware River and improved the colony's military and commercial prospects by building Fort Elfsborg, near modern Salem on the New Jersey side of the river, to seal the Delaware against English and Dutch ships. Yet Printz managed to strengthen his colony while living peacefully with his neighbors.

The Dutch had made the first trading contacts in the Delaware Valley and the Swedish settlement was a commercial and possibly a military threat to New Netherland. Perhaps the Dutch tolerated the Swedes because New Netherland's relations with its Indian neighbors often degenerated into open warfare. Another reason may have been that the generally cordial relations among England, the Netherlands and Sweden in Europe extended to their colonies in the New World.

In 1654 Printz was succeeded by a somewhat less judicious governor, Johan Rising. New Netherland was then governed by the energetic Peter Stuyvesant. Soon after arriving in the New World, Rising attempted to dislodge the Dutch from the valley by seizing Fort Casimir (New Castle, Delaware), below Fort Christina on the western shore of the river. Stuyvesant responded by attacking New Sweden late in the summer of 1655. The virtually bloodless Dutch conquest ended Swedish sovereignty—though not the Swedish and Finnish presence—in the Delaware Valley.

While Swedes and Finns continued to settle in New Jersey, Delaware and Pennsylvania, they did not begin to arrive in the United States in large numbers until after 1840.

Swedish immigration was highest between 1867 and 1914 due to poor local economic conditions in Sweden and the availability of cheap land in the American west. At the peak of immigration in the 1880s, an average of 37,000 Swedes came to the United States each year. Most of the new settlers bypassed New Sweden and headed west to Minnesota, Illinois, Iowa, Kansas, Nebraska, Texas, California, and Washington, which remain the states with the largest numbers of Swedish-Americans today.

LENDERS TO THE EXHIBITION

American Swedish Historical
  Foundation-Museum
Mr. Bo Erhner
Etnografiska Museet
Rare Book Collections,
  Firestone Library, Princeton
  University
Higgins Armory Museum
Jonkoping Lans Museum
Memory of Linnea Zackariasson
Nationalmuseum
New Jersey State Archives
Nordiska Museet
Philadelphia Maritime Museum
Pierpont Morgan Library
Riksarkivet
Special Collections and
  Archives, Rutgers University
  Libraries
Skoklosters Slott
State Museum of Pennsylvania

CHRONOLOGY

1607-20	The English begin to settle Virginia and New England.
1609-24	The Dutch begin to explore and settle New Netherland.
1618-48	The Thirty Years' War. At various times both Sweden and the Netherlands are combatants.
1621	The Dutch West India Company is founded, in large part to colonize and exploit New Netherland.
1620s-30s	The English and the Dutch explore the Delaware River and its bay. While each claims the region, neither plants a permanent settlement, though the Dutch attempt to.
1624	William Usselinx visits Sweden and discusses the idea of a colonial venture with Swedish officials, including King Gustavus Adolphus (Gustav II Adolf). Usselinx receives a charter for a general Swedish trading company "for Asia, Africa, America, and Magellenica." The king purchases shares in the company and lends his name to a campaign to raise money for it among the Swedish nobility. But the Swedish trading company languishes throughout the 1620s for lack of capital and because the king and his chief minister, Axel Oxenstierna, are distracted by European matters, especially the Thirty Years' War, which Sweden enters in 1630.
1624	The Dutch settle a handful of people on Burlington Island in the Delaware. By 1630 the settlers have moved back to New Amsterdam.
1626	The Dutch establish a trading post, Fort Nassau, at the site of present Gloucester, New Jersey, but they garrison it only intermittently.
1631	The Dutch found Swanendael on the western shore of Delaware Bay. It is destroyed by Indians in the same year.
1632	Gustavus Adolphus is killed during the battle of Leutzen. He is succeeded as Swedish monarch by his six-year-old daughter Christina. Sweden is governed by a regency during the queen's

minority, with Oxenstierna the effective head of state. He is instrumental in reviving the idea of a colonial venture.

1635   Samuel Blommaert, like Usselinx an original stockholder of the Dutch West India Company and a Swanendael investor, proposes a colonial scheme to the Swedes. It is Blommaert's plan—essentially—which is adopted two years later.

1635-36   Blommaert selects Peter Minuit to lead a settlement to the Delaware Valley, once a colony is chartered. Minuit had been the governor of New Netherland in the late 1620s and the early 1630s and is familiar with the Delaware Valley.

1637   In August, the Swedish government charters the New Sweden Company. Many of the stockholders are Dutch or German, but they also include such Swedish grandees as Oxenstierna and members of his family. Early in November, *Kalmar Nyckel* and *Fogel Grip* sail from Gothenburg (Goteborg). On the voyage to the Netherlands both ships sustain severe damage. In December they arrive at Texel in the Netherlands to be repaired and outfitted for the voyage to America. On December 31, *Kalmar Nyckel* and *Fogel Grip* sail for America.

1638   The Swedes and Finns arrive in the Delaware Valley sometime in March. They found Fort Christina, the colony's main settlement, and the first permanent European settlement in the Delaware valley. Minuit purchases land from the Susquehannock Indians and perhaps from the Lenape as well. On the return voyage, Minuit is lost at sea.

1640   Peter Hollander Ridder arrives in New Sweden in April and assumes the governorship.

1640-41   The Swedes extend the limits of New Sweden from the Schuylkill River to the falls at present Trenton. Ridder buys land from the Indians that extends from Raccoon Creek east to Cape May. English from New Haven Colony settle near Salem Creek (Varkens or Varkins Kill) on territory claimed by the Swedes.

1641   In February, the Swedish government buys out the foreign shareholders in the New Sweden Company.

1642-60	The English Civil War and the Commonwealth. Relations between England and Sweden are cordial throughout the period.
1643	Johan Printz arrives in New Sweden and assumes the governorship. He builds Fort Elfsborg on the New Jersey side of the Delaware to seal the river to the Dutch and the English. The fort was probably near Salem Creek; its exact location still eludes searchers.
1643-53	The decade of Printz's governorship is the colony's most prosperous time. Farming settlements are planted up and down both sides of the river in modern Delaware, Pennsylvania and New Jersey, and in Maryland, and Printz builds his headquarters, Printzhof, at Tinicum Island, near present Philadelphia. He absorbs the English at Salem Creek into the Swedish colony. While New Sweden is never self-sufficient, and is constantly harrassed by the Dutch, Printz maintains it by his energy and the force of his flamboyant personality.
1644	Christina reaches her majority and assumes personal rule of Sweden.
1648	The Peace of Westphalia ends the Thirty Years' War. The Swedes abandon Fort Elfsborg.
1651	The Dutch build Fort Casimir at the site of modern New Castle, Delaware.
1653	When his repeated requests for recall are ignored, Printz returns to Sweden, leaving the colony without a governor.
1654	Johan Rising arrives in New Sweden to assume the governorship. On May 21, Rising captures Fort Casimir from the Dutch and renames it Fort Trinity. Christina abdicates and is succeeded by her cousin, Karl X Gustav. Karl Gustav is immediately preoccupied with war with Denmark. Axel Oxenstierna dies in November.
1655	The Dutch retaliate for the Swedish attack on Fort Casimir. On September 1, Governor Peter Stuyvesant recaptures Fort Trinity and seizes Fort Christina, ending Swedish sovereignty in the Delaware Valley.

1655-74	The Dutch govern the Delaware Valley until they in turn are conquered by the English in 1664—as bloodlessly as they had conquered the Swedes. The Dutch briefly regain New Netherland in 1674, but are again—and finally—ejected by the English. The Swedes and the Finns remain on the Delaware.
1693	Swedes and Finns in the Delaware Valley petition Sweden's King Karl XI to send them Lutheran priests, hymnals, prayer books, and catechisms, to help them to preserve their Lutheran faith and their language.
1697	In June, the first three priests of the new Swedish mission to America—Anders Rudman, Erik Bjork, and Jonas Auren—arrive in the Delaware Valley. Thereafter the mission is continuously resupplied with pastors throughout the 18th century, including Andreas Hesselius, Israel Acrelius, and Nils Collin. The mission helps to maintain a "cultural" New Sweden long after the political end of the colony.
1831	With the death of Nils Collin, pastor of Old Swedes (Gloria Dei) Church in Philadelphia, the Swedish Lutheran mission to the Delaware Valley ends, as does cultural New Sweden.

THE NEW SWEDEN COLONY
Catalogue of Exhibition

SWEDEN IN THE 17TH CENTURY
CLIMATE FOR COLONIALISM

Colonialism was in the air throughout northern Europe during the 17th century. It was an age of discovery and expansion—in the arts, science and industry. Europeans tried to spread their commercial and political dominion throughout the world. Inspired by the riches Spain and Portugal had won from their colonies in the New World, Sweden, England and the Netherlands competed throughout the first half of the century for control of the middle Atlantic seaboard of North America.

While we are used to thinking of the English and the Dutch as 17th-century colonial powers, we do not as readily associate Sweden with early European colonialism. The Sweden of 1620 to 1720 was, however, a European Great Power. Her continental possessions made the Baltic Sea a Swedish lake. At various times Sweden controlled Finland, portions of modern Poland, Latvia, Estonia, Lithuania, the Soviet Union and even northern portions of Germany. In the middle years of the century the Swedes controlled trade in the Baltic Sea and were one of the major military and political combatants in Germany during the Thirty Years' War (1618-1648), after entering the war in 1630. As early as 1624 Gustavus Adolphus encouraged the efforts of Willem Usselinx, a Dutch West India Company director, to found a Swedish overseas trading company— the South Company. The South Company soon failed because the Swedes lacked investment capital. But Axel Oxenstierna remained keenly interested in a colonial venture to raise money for Sweden. In 1637, the Chancellor supported a proposal by Samuel Blommaert, another Dutch West India Company director, for a Swedish colony in North America.

In 1637 the New Sweden Company, with heavy Dutch financial support, sent its first two ships to the middle Atlantic seaboard. Peter Minuit commanded the expedition. He had been the Director-General of the Dutch colony of New Netherland from 1626 to 1631. Sweden was about to join Spain, France, England and the Netherlands in the general European effort to extract riches from the New World. The Swedes set sail for Delaware Bay in search of furs and tobacco.

Portrait of Queen Christina as a child by J.H. Elbfas
Courtesy of the Nationalmuseum, Stockholm

GUSTAVUS ADOLPHUS BUILDS AN EMPIRE ON THE BALTIC

The great King, whose zeal for the honor of God was not less ardent than for the welfare of his subjects....

Israel Acrelius, 1759

Gustavus Adolphus (1594-1632) was recognized throughout Europe as a military genius in his own time. From the beginning of his reign in 1611 until his death at the Battle of Leutzen in 1632, Sweden was mostly at war. He continued the House of Vasa's acquisition of territory around the Baltic Sea and, in 1630, he entered the Thirty Years' War as the Protestant champion against the Catholic forces of the Holy Roman Empire. Gustavus Adolphus reorganized the government of Sweden, including the army and navy. His success on the battlefields of Europe spread his military innovations and brought Sweden recognition as a Great Power. Even the Battle of Leutzen, at which he was killed, was a Swedish victory.

1. Gustavus Adolphus
    engraving
    w.42cm., h.55cm.
    Willem Jacobsz Delff after
    Michiel Jansz van Miervelt
    (1580-1638)
    Sweden
    Lent by the Nationalmuseum,
      Stockholm

2. Sword
    wood, metal
    h. 87cm.
    17th century
    Northern Sweden
    57.535
    Lent by the Nordiska Museet,
      Stockholm

STOCKHOLM IN THE 17TH CENTURY AS
DRAWN BY ERIK DAHLBERG
Courtesy of the Nationalmuseum, Stockholm

Sweden, the Nation's History by Franklin D. Scott (1977) University of Minnesota Press

3

3. Breastplate
   steel, iron, brass
   w.37.8 cm., h.46.5cm., d.14.4cm.
   1620-1625
   Probably Holland
   Acc. 15
   Lent by the Higgins Armory
     Museum, Worcester, Mass.

   Well into the 17th century Sweden was heavily dependent upon imported arms and armor, particularly from Holland. Very similar breastplates are shown worn by infantrymen in Adam van Breen's *De Nassausche Wapen-Handelinge* (1618), and Dutch pieces which were captured by English troops in 1627 are preserved in the Royal Armouries, H. M. Tower of London. Although the use of metal body armor in Europe had entered into a period of steady decline by the time of Sweden's participation in the Thirty Years' War, it remained popular with colonists in America. Steel breastplates such as this provided an excellent defense from the arrows of the Native Americans.

4. Cabasset Helmet
   steel, iron, brass, leather
   h.22.3cm., w.24.9cm., d.32.3cm.
   1600-1650
   Germany or Austria
   Acc. 442
   Lent by the Higgins Armory
     Museum, Worcester, Mass.

   Light, open-faced helmets were produced in the thousands for European armies during the late 16th through mid 17th centuries. Such practical headgear was widely adopted by infantry of the period. The flat brim and unrestricted field of vision afforded by the cabasset made it popular with musketeers who required a defense that did not interfere with aiming.

QUEEN CHRISTINA AND THE REGENCY

Gustavus Adolphus' death in 1632 left his only child, the six-year-old Queen Christina, on the Swedish throne. The King had left instructions that she was to be raised to rule, making Christina's education like that of a 17th-century prince. She grew up strong-willed and well educated, with a knowledge of Latin and Greek, philosophy and science. During her minority, until 1644, the country was ruled by a regency headed by Axel Oxenstierna, Sweden's Chancellor.Oxenstierna, a great statesman, had been responsible for much of Sweden's internal government under the late King, who was often out of the country at war.

Queen and Chancellor struggled for power, each with a different vision of Sweden's greatness. Oxenstierna shared the King's view of Sweden as a political and military and growing economic power. For Christina, Sweden's greatness lay in imported high culture, an opulent court and nobles whose lifestyles rivaled their French counterparts. By the time she abdicated in 1654, her lavish spending had helped to put Sweden deeply in debt.

5. Terence's *Comoediae* from Queen
    Christina's Library
    ink, paper, leather, gilt
    l.30cm., w.23cm., d.4cm.
    1642
    Paris
    Lent by the Pierpont Morgan
    Library
    With the arms of Queen Christina
    on the cover

6. One Ore Coin of Queen Christina
    silver
    d.19mm.
    1634
    Sweden
    Lent in memory of Linnea
    Zackariasson

7. One Quarter Ore Coin Of Queen
    Christina
    copper
    d.29mm.
    1636
    Sweden
    Lent in memory of Linnea
    Zackariasson

No mint mark appears, but mints in Sweden are known to have been located at Avesta, Nykoping and Sater

8. One Mark (Eight Ore) Coin of
    Queen Christina
    silver
    d.26mm.
    Undated, believed to be 1651
    Sweden
    Lent in memory of Linnea
    Zackariasson

9. *Suecia Antiqua Et Hodierna* by Erik
    Dahlber
    ink, paper
    w.44cm., h.34cm., d.9cm.
    1667-1716
    Stockholm
    Lent by the American Swedish
    Historical Foundation-Museum,
    Philadelphia

5

10

10. Axel Oxenstierna
    engraving
    w.42cm., h.55cm.
    Willem Jacobsz Delff after
    Michiel Jansz van Miervelt
    (1580-1638)
    Sweden
    Lent by the Nationalmuseum,
      Stockholm

25

NEW LIFESTYLES FOR
ROYALTY AND ARISTOCRACY

...the liberal arts, expelled from the countries where they formerly flourished...would find refuge in the North.

Professor Menius of Dorpat,

1632

Sweden's wars of expansion and her participation in the Thirty Years' War brought the Swedish aristocracy new wealth from the conquered territories and exposure to the more lavish lifestyles of the nobles of continental Europe. Queen Christina's interest in increasing the grandeur of her court at Tre Kronor palace and her royal city of Stockholm encouraged the nobles' development of a more ostentatious mode of living in the city.

Swedish nobles began to build lavish townhouses in Stockholm. On their country estates they built chateaus in the French manner. Both town and country houses were richly furnished, often with goods imported from the Netherlands and the German states. Extravagant displays of wealth became the norm for court and nobles, although Sweden remained for the first half of the 17th century a country with little commerce or industry, wealthy in land but not in money.

11. Wall Sconce
    chased brass
    w.36cm., h.46cm.
    17th century (?)
    Sweden
    52.534
    Lent by the Nordiska Museet,
    Stockholm

12. Gilded Leather "Wallpaper"
    gilt paint on leather
    w.112cm., h.45cm.
    late 17th century
    Sweden
    101.850
    Lent by the Nordiska Museet,
    Stockholm

13. Fireback
    cast iron
    w.66.5cm., h.99cm.
    inscribed "anno 1632 Gustawus
    Adolph D.B. Svecia"
    Sweden
    46.600
    Lent by the Nordiska Museet,
    Stockholm

14. Candle Stick
    brass
    h.24cm., d.15.5
    17th century
    Sweden
    19.401
    Lent by the Nordiska Museet,
    Stockholm

15. Knife and Fork Picturing Gustavus
    Adolphus II
    steel, silver, enamel
    l.19.2cm., w.18cm.
    ca. 1650
    Sweden
    265.996 a,b
    Lent by the Nordiska Museet,
    Stockholm

16. Folding Knife Used at Banquets
    steel, brass
    l. 9cm.
    17th century
    44.485 a-b
    Lent by the Nordiska Museet,
    Stockholm

Makalos, Stockholm, townhouse of the De LaGardie family in the 17th century
Courtesy of the Livrustkammaren, Stockholm

19

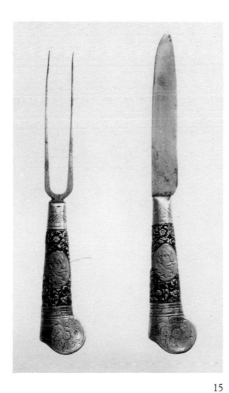

15

17. Drinking Bowl
painted wood, gilded
d. 22cm.
17th-century style
Sweden
48.601
Lent by the Nordiska Museet,
  Stockholm

Inscribed "Empty no man praises me
  but full I am taken..."

18. Tankard
curly-grained birchwood
w.25.5cm., h.32cm.
17th-century style
Fellingsbro parish, Vastmonland
78.271
Lent by the Nordiska Museet,
  Stockholm

19. "The Rich Man's Supper"
  Wallhanging
paint on canvas
l.292cm., h.120cm.
part of a suite dated 1645
Alfta parish, Halsningland, Sweden
199.675
Lent by the Nordiska Museet,
  Stockholm

20. Bedcover
blue silk taffeta, embroidered with
black silk
l.187.5cm., w.155cm.
Dated 1630
Sweden
192.040
Lent by the Nordiska Museet,
  Stockholm

Embroidered Weapons Of
  Horn-Oxenstierna, Count Gustaf
  Horn of Bjorneborg (1592-1657)
  married 1628 to the Baroness
  Christina Oxenstierna (1612-1681)

THE DELAWARE RIVER VALLEY IN THE 17TH CENTURY
SETTING FOR A COLONIAL VENTURE

The Delaware River Valley was opened to European exploration and trade with the Indians by Henry Hudson's voyage of 1609. In the succeeding decades, the river was visited by Dutch and English ships bearing glass beads and metal tools to trade with the Indians for beaver and otter pelts. The fur trade led the Dutch at New Amsterdam, now New York City, to establish a small post, Fort Nassau, on the Delaware River a little south of what is today Camden. The Dutch used the post only intermittently, and they established no permanent settlements in the Delaware Valley. But they claimed the river as a part of New Netherland and called it the South River.

The English and Dutch traders who visited the river bought furs not only from the local Indians (whom the English called the Delaware and the Swedes called the Renappi), but also from the Indians of the Susquehanna River Valley of present Pennsylvania. These Indians, called the Minquas by the Dutch and the Swedes, and the Susquehannock by the English, came to the Delaware River to trade. They competed, often violently, with the Delaware Indians for access to the prized metal tools and guns offered by the Europeans.

Indian Family drawn by Per Lindestrom
ca. 1655
Courtesy of the Riksarkivet, Stockholm

THE INDIANS OF THE
DELAWARE RIVER VALLEY

During the summer they have no

certain dwellings, but move about

here and there around the country.

However, in the fall each and every

sachem has a house built for

himself, which he and his subjects

can live in during the winter...

Per Lindestrom, 1654-1656

The Indians we today call the Delaware were in the early 1600s a number of small groups living along the streams which flow into the Delaware River. They called themselves by a variety of names which are recorded on early European maps: Sanhican, Armewamen, Naraticon, Mantaes and Sewapois. The Dutch and the Swedes called them the Indians of "the River," and the Swedes eventually called them the Renappi. Each group was politically independent, but all spoke dialects of the Algonkian language and practiced a seasonal round of food-getting activities with a stone-age technology. They located their unfortified villages of scattered longhouses along the streams where the soils could be farmed with wooden digging sticks and hoes tipped with bone, stone or shell blades. They hunted the white-tailed deer for food throughout the year. Wild plant foods, shellfish and seasonally migratory fish and waterfowl were also sources of food.

21. Celt
    black slate
    l.6.5cm., w.5cm., d.2cm.
    Green Swamp Site
    Cumberland County, New Jersey
    Delaware Indians
    NJSM 36

22. Celt
    stone
    l.8cm., w.4.5cm., d.2.5cm.
    Burlington County, New Jersey
    Delaware Indians
    NJSM 704

23. Nutting Stone
    sandstone
    l.16cm., w.10cm., h.5cm.
    Abbott Farm Site
    Mercer County, New Jersey
    Delaware Indians
    NJSM Acc. 788
    Gift of Princeton University
    Museum of Natural History

24. Hand Grinding Stone
    sandstone
    l.11cm., w.8cm., h.4cm.
    Abbott Farm Site
    Mercer County, New Jersey
    Delaware Indians
    NJSM Acc. 788
    Gift of Princeton University
    Museum of Natural History

25. Grinding Slab
    sandstone
    l.29.5cm., w.26cm., h.9cm.
    Abbott Farm Site
    Mercer County, New Jersey
    Delaware Indians
    NJSM Acc. 788
    Gift of Princeton University
    Museum of Natural History

32

34

33

26. Scraper
    chert
    l.4cm., w.3cm., h.1.5cm.
    Abbott Farm Site
    Mercer County, New Jersey
    Delaware Indians
    NJSM Acc. 788
    Gift of Princeton University
    Museum of Natural History

27. Knife
    chert
    l.10.2cm., w.4.5cm., d.3cm.
    Abbott Farm Site
    Mercer County, New Jersey
    Delaware Indians
    NJSM Acc. 788
    Gift of Princeton University
    Museum of Natural History

28. Net Sinkers (6)
    sandstone
    average 7.5cm., w.5cm., d.2cm.
    Abbott Farm Site
    Mercer County, New Jersey
    Delaware Indians
    NJSM Acc. 788
    Gift of Princeton University
    Museum of Natural History

29. Projectile Points (3)
    chert, sandstone
    Green Swamp Site
    Cumberland County, New Jersey
    Delaware Indians
    NJSM 31, 32, 34

30. Pestle
    sandstone
    l.33cm., d.6cm.
    Camden County, New Jersey
    Delaware Indians
    NJSM 656

31. Awl
    bone
    l.8.5cm.
    Green Swamp Site
    Cumberland County, New Jersey
    Delaware Indians
    NJSM 42

32. Fish Hook
    bone
    l. 5.5cm.
    Gloucester County, New Jersey
    Delaware Indians
    NJSM 313 b.18

40

37

33. Effigy Face
ceramic
w.4cm.,h.4.5cm.
Mercer County, New Jersey
Delaware Indians
NJSM 1825

34. Carved Pendant in Shape of an
   Animal
stone
l. 4.3cm.
Gloucester County, New Jersey
Delaware Indians
NJSM 344

35. Pendant
shale
l.3.5cm.,w.2.5cm.
Gloucester County, New Jersey
Delaware Indians
NJSM 666

36. Pot Rim Fragment
clay
l.5.5cm.,h.5cm.
Indian Head Site
Salem County, New Jersey
Delaware Indians
NJSM 26946

37. Small Vessel
clay
h.16.5cm.
Johnson Site
Cumberland County, New Jersey
Delaware Indians
NJSM 27736 a

38. Pipe
ceramic
l.9cm.
Pemberton
Burlington County, New Jersey
Delaware Indians
NJSM 66.652

39. Pipe
ceramic
l.8cm.
Millville
Cumberland County, New Jersey
Delaware Indians
NJSM 66.563

40. Pipe
ceramic
l.16.5cm.
Murray Farm Site
Burlington County, New Jersey
Delaware Indians
NJSM 1307

41. Ax
sandstone
l.20cm.,w.10.5cm.,d.4.5cm.
early 1600s
Susquehanna Valley, Pennsylvania
Susquehannock Indians
B. 161
Lent by the State Museum of
   Pennsylvania

THE INDIANS OF THE
SUSQUEHANNA RIVER VALLEY

The Minquas, who are yet faithful

to us and call themselves our

protectors...

Johan Rising, 1655

The Indians who have come to be known as the Susquehannock were Iroquoian-speaking groups who lived in the lower Susquehanna River Valley of Pennsylvania. They were called the Minquas by the Dutch and English traders who visited the Delaware River in the early 1600s, a name by which the Swedes also knew them. While their lifestyle was similar technologically to that of the Delaware Indians, the Susquehannock were organized into larger political units of thousands of people who lived in fortified villages.

During the 1620s and 1630s the Susquehannock traveled down the Schuylkill and Christina Rivers to reach the Dutch and English ships trading in the Delaware River Valley. They raided the Delaware Indians to drive the latter away from the river banks and gain control of all Native American trade with the Europeans in the Delaware Valley. The Susquehannock were largely successful in this because their large war parties could retreat, if necessary, to the safety of their fortified villages.

42. Arrowpoints
stone
1645-1665
Strickler Site
Lancaster County, Pennsylvania
Susquehannock Indians
LA 3/472 a
Lent by the State Museum of
Pennsylvania

43. Awl
bone
l. 5cm.
1575-1600
Schultz Site
Lancaster County, Pennsylvania
Susquehannock Indians
LA 7-1/401
Lent by the State Museum of
Pennsylvania

44. Harpoon Tip
antler
1.21cm., w.2.5cm., d..75cm.
1575-1600
Schultz Site
Lancaster County, Pennsylvania
Susquehannock Indians

LA 7-2/265
Lent by the State Museum of
Pennsylvania

45. Fish Hook
bone
1.3cm.
1575-1600
Schultz Site
Lancaster County, Pennsylvania
Susquehannock Indians
LA 7-1/592
Lent by the State Museum of
Pennsylvania

46. End Scraper
quartz
l. 5.5cm., w. 3.5cm., h. 2cm.
1575-1600
Funk/Schultz Site
Lancaster County, Pennsylvania
LA 9/116
Lent by the State Museum of
Pennsylvania

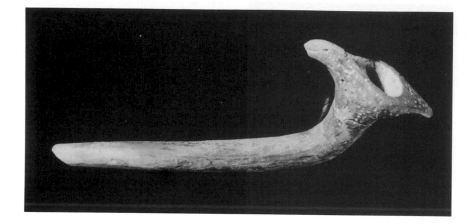

62

Susquehannock Indian as drawn on John
Smith's map of Virginia

47. Pestle
    sandstone
    l.30cm.,d.5.5cm.
    17th century
    Susquehanna Valley, Pennsylvania
    Susquehannock Indians
    uncat.
    Lent by the State Museum of
      Pennsylvania
    Used for pounding corn into meal

48. Bell Pestle
    granitic stone
    l.11.2cm., d.8.1cm.
    17th century
    Susquehanna Valley, Pennsylvania
    Susquehannock Indians
    I 566
    Lent by the State Museum of
      Pennsylvania

49. Ladle
    bone
    l.15cm., d.18.5cm.
    1575-1600
    Funk/Schultz Site
    Lancaster County, Pennsylvania
    Susquehannock Indians
    LA 9/128
    Lent by the State Museum of
      Pennsylvania

50. Spoon with Animal Effigy Handle
    wood
    l.11.1cm., h.6.2cm.
    1645-1665
    Strickler Site
    Lancaster County, Pennsylvania
    Susquehannock Indians
    LA 3/521
    Lent by the State Museum of
      Pennsylvania

51. Double-Mouthed Washington
      Boro Incised Pot
    clay
    h.7.9cm., w.12.5cm.
    17th century
    Susquehanna Valley, Pennsylvania
    Susquehannock Indians
    B. 9
    Lent by the State Museum of
      Pennsylvania

52. Toy Pot With Schultz Incised
      Decoration
    clay
    h.6.3cm., d.6.8cm.
    17th century
    Susquehanna Valley, Pennsylvania
    Susquehannock Indians
    B. 75
    Lent by the State Museum
      of Pennsylvania

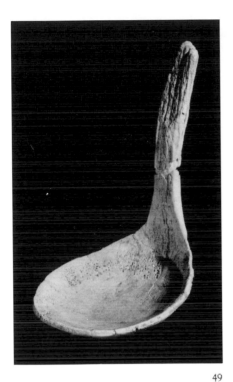

49

53. Toy Pot with Incised
    Decoration
    clay
    h.3.5cm., d.3.5cm.
    17th century
    Susquehanna Valley, Pennsylvania
    Susquehannock Indians
    856
    Lent by the State Museum of
    Pennsylvania

54. Washington Boro Incised Pot
    clay
    h.19.8cm., d.16cm.
    early 1600s
    Washington Boro Site
    Lancaster County, Pennsylvania
    Susquehannock Indians
    B. 101
    Lent by the State Museum of
    Pennsylvania

55. Grinding Slab
    siltstone
    l.28cm., w.26cm., h.5cm.
    17th century
    Susquehanna Valley, Pennsylvania
    Susquehannock Indians
    Lent by the State Museum of
    Pennsylvania

56. Milling Stone
    sandstone
    d. 9cm.
    1645-1665
    Strickler Site
    Lancaster County, Pennsylvania
    Susquehannock Indians
    LA 3/501
    Lent by the State Museum of
    Pennsylvania

57. Parched Corn
    17th century
    Susquehanna Valley, Pennsylvania
    lA 36.6
    Lent by the State Museum of
    Pennsylvania

58. Charred Corn Cobs
    1575-1600
    Funk/Schultz Site
    Lancaster County, Pennsylvania
    LA 9
    Lent by the State Museum of
    Pennsylvania

59. Pumpkin Seeds
    1645-1665
    Strickler Site
    Lancaster County, Pennsylvania
    LA 3/31
    Lent by the State Museum of
    Pennsylvania

60. Pipe
    painted clay
    l.17.5cm., d.2.5cm.
    1645-1665
    Strickler Site
    Lancaster County, Pennsylvania
    Susquehannock Indians
    LA 3/472 b
    Lent by the State Museum of
    Pennsylvania

61. Tulip Bowl Pipe
    clay
    l.15cm., d.2.5cm.
    1645-1665
    Strickler Site
    Lancaster County, Pennsylvania
    Susquehannock Indians
    LA 3/540
    Lent by the State Museum of
    Pennsylvania

62. Bird Effigy Pipe
    clay
    l.12.5cm., d.3.2cm.
    early 1600s
    Frey-Haverstick Site
    Lancaster County, Pennsylvania
    Susquehannock Indians
    LA 6/96
    Lent by the State Museum of
    Pennsylvania

68

51

63. Spotted Bird Effigy Pipe
    clay
    l. 18cm., d. 3cm.
    1645-1665
    Strickler site
    Lancaster County, Pennsylvania
    Susquehannock Indians
    LA 3/451 b
    Lent by the State Museum of
    Pennsylvania

64. Masquette
    schist
    w. 1.7cm., h. 2cm.
    17th century
    Byrd Leibhart Site
    York County, Pennsylvania
    Susquehannock Indians
    YO 170/65
    Lent by the State Museum of
    Pennsylvania

65. Masquette
    steatite
    l. 3cm., w. 2.5cm.
    17th century
    Susquehanna Valley,
    Pennsylvania
    Susquehannock Indians
    2/591
    Lent by the State Museum of
    Pennsylvania

66. Turtle Figure
    steatite
    l. 4cm., w. 2.5cm., h. 1.2cm.
    17th century
    Susquehanna Valley,
    Pennsylvania
    Susquehannock Indians
    B. 232
    Lent by the State Museum of
    Pennsylvania

67. Turtle Figure
    bone
    l. 3cm., w. 2cm.
    17th century
    Susquehanna Valley,
    Pennsylvania
    Susquehannock Indians
    B. 234

Lent by the State Museum of
Pennsylvania

68. Human Figure
    steatite
    l. 9.5cm., w. 4cm.
    17th century
    Susquehanna Valley,
    Pennsylvania
    Susquehannock Indians
    B. 236
    Lent by the State Museum of
    Pennsylvania

69. Beads (10)
    elk teeth
    1575-1600
    Schultz Site
    Lancaster County, Pennsylvania
    Susquehannock Indians
    LA 7-2/314
    Lent by the State Museum of
    Pennsylvania

70. Beads (3)
    deer phalanges
    1575-1600
    Schultz Site
    Lancaster County, Pennsylvania
    Susquehannock Indians
    LA 7-1/896/686/561
    Lent by the State Museum of
    Pennsylvania

71. Beads (20)
    bird bone
    1575-1600
    Schultz Site
    Lancaster County, Pennsylvania
    Susquehannock Indians
    LA 7
    Lent by the State Museum of
    Pennsylvania

72. Gorget
    shell
    l. 7cm., w. 7.5cm.
    1575-1600
    Funk/Schultz Site
    Lancaster County, Pennsylvania
    LA 9/116
    Lent by the State Museum of
    Pennsylvania

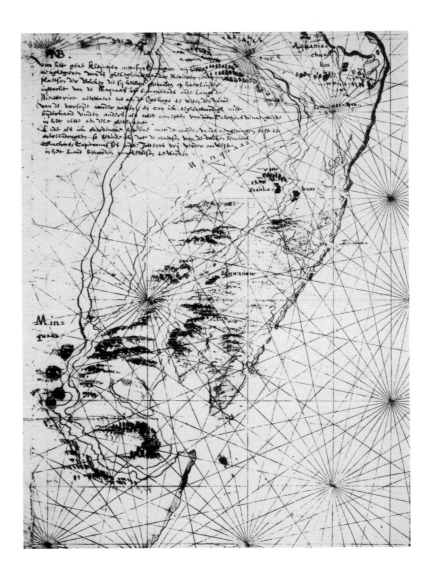

Dutch map of the Atlantic coast showing
what is now New Jersey in the early 1600s
Courtesy of the Kungliga Biblioteket, Stockholm

73. Disk Beads
    shell
    middle 1600s
    Strickler Site
    Lancaster County, Pennsylvania
    LA 3/7
    Lent by the State Museum of
    　Pennsylvania

74. Rattle
    turtle shell
    l. 12cm., w. 10cm., h. 6.5cm.
    1575—1600
    Funk/Schultz Site
    Lancaster County, Pennsylvania
    LA 9/151
    Lent by the State Museum of
    　Pennsylvania

INDIANS AND EUROPEANS
COMPETE FOR TRADE

...three Indians of the Armewamen

came before the yacht. They told us

that they were fugitives—that the

Minquas had killed some of their

people...

David DeVries, 1633

The Native Americans of the Atlantic seaboard were not mainly interested in the glass beads and trinkets the European traders brought, although they used the beads and trinkets for decorating clothing and as ornaments. Much more important to the Indians were the guns and metal tools the traders were willing to exchange for beaver and otter skins. The Indians could not produce metal tools themselves, having a stone technology. The iron knives, hoes, hatchets and guns made the Indians' hunting and farming much more productive.

As European ships appeared in the rivers of eastern North America, Indian groups moved toward them, eager to trade. The Delaware River Valley was no exception to this pattern. As Dutch and English ships came to trade in the river in the 1620s and 1630s conflict between the Susquehannock and Delaware Indians increased as each sought to control access to the European tools and guns.

75. Pistol Barrel
     iron
     l.25.5cm., d.2.5cm.
     early 1600s
     Frey-Haverstick Site
     Lancaster County, Pennsylvania
     LA 6/94
     Lent by the State Museum of
        Pennsylvania

76. Pistol Flintlock
     iron
     l.12.8cm., w.2.5cm., h.6.8cm.
     early 1600s
     Frey-Haverstick Site
     Lancaster County, Pennsylvania
     LA 6/94
     Lent by the State Museum of
        Pennsylvania

77. Gunflint
     chert
     l.3.5cm.,h.3cm.,w..5cm.
     17th century
     Monmouth County, New Jersey
     NJSM 2102

78. Hoe Blade
     iron
     l. 18cm., w. 15.5cm., h. 6cm.
     middle 1600s
     Strickler Site
     Lancaster County, Pennsylvania
     LA 3/518
     Lent by the State Museum of
        Pennsylvania

79. Small Belt Axe
     iron
     l. 13cm., w. 2.5cm.
     mid 1600s
     Strickler Site
     Lancaster County, Pennsylvania
     LA 3/571
     Lent by the State Museum of
        Pennsylvania

86

80. Small Hammer Head
    iron
    l. 9cm., w. 2.4cm., h. 2.3cm.
    middle 1600s
    Strickler Site
    Lancaster County, Pennsylvania
    LA 3/315
    Lent by the State Museum of
      Pennsylvania

81. Celt Head
    iron
    l. 8.5cm., w. 1.2cm.
    1575-1600
    Schultz Site
    Lancaster County, Pennsylvania
    LA 7/358
    Lent by the State Museum of
      Pennsylvania

82. Harpoon Tip
    iron
    l. 21cm., w. 3cm.
    middle 1600s
    Strickler Site
    Lancaster County, Pennsylvania
    LA 3/611
    Lent by the State Museum of
      Pennsylvania

83. Awl
    iron
    l. 7cm.
    middle 1600s
    Strickler Site
    Lancaster County, Pennsylvania
    LA 3/86
    Lent by the State Museum of
      Pennsylvania

84. Delft Pendant
    made from a delft dish
    d. 3.5cm.
    early 1600s
    Frey-Haverstick Site
    Lancaster County, Pennsylvania
    LA 6/110
    Lent by the State Museum of
      Pennsylvania

85. Spoon
    latten
    l. 5.1cm., w. 17.5cm.
    Holland
    Frey-Haverstick Site
    Lancaster County, Pennsylvania
    LA 6/97
    Lent by the State Museum of
      Pennsylvania

86. Bagpiper Knife Handle
    cast bronze
    l.7cm.,w.2cm.,d.1.6cm.
    early 1600s
    Frey-Haverstick Site
    Lancaster County, Pennsylvania
    LA 6/116
    Lent by the State Museum of
      Pennsylvania

87. Mouth Harp
    brass
    l. 5.5cm., w. 3.3cm.
    middle 1600s
    Strickler Site
    Lancaster County, Pennsylvania
    LA 3/319
    Lent by the State Museum of
      Pennsylvania

94

88. Snuff Box
    brass
    l.6.6cm., w.5cm., h.3.7cm.
    1634 (marked)
    Holland
    Byrd Leibhart Site
    York County, Pennsylvania
    YO 170/114
    Lent by the State Museum of
        Pennsylvania

89. Tobacco Box with Tamper and
        Lid
    brass
    h.5cm., d.6.5cm.
    17th century
    Susquehanna Valley, Pennsylvania
    LA 6/99
    Lent by the State Museum of
        Pennsylvania

90. Trade Pipe
    brass
    l. 12cm., w. 10cm., h. 6.5cm.
    early 1600s
    Frey-Haverstick Site
    Lancaster County, Pennsylvania
    LA 6/115 a
    Lent by the State Museum of
        Pennsylvania

91. Tobacco Pipe
    tan clay
    l.13cm., d.1.5cm.
    early 1600s
    Frey-Haverstick Site
    Lancaster County, Pennsylvania
    LA 6/116
    Lent by the State Museum of
        Pennsylvania

92. Tobacco Pipe
    white clay
    l.11.1cm., d..8cm.
    mid 1600s
    Byrd Leibhart Site
    York County, Pennsylvania
    YO 170/114
    Lent by the State Museum of
        Pennsylvania

93. Tobacco Pipe
    white clay
    l.16.5cm., d.1.9cm.
    17th century
    Martins Creek, Pennsylvania
    NJSM 2492

94. Case Bottle
    glass
    h.19.5cm., d.8cm.
    17th century
    Strickler Site
    Lancaster County, Pennsylvania
    LA 3/22
    Lent by the State Museum of
        Pennsylvania

95. Bottle Fragment With Seal Mark "BM"
    glass
    d.4.5cm.
    mid 1600s
    Strickler Site
    Lancaster County, Pennsylvania
    LA 3/519
    Lent by the State Museum of
        Pennsylvania

96. Green Goblet Stem with Spiral Design
    glass
    l.8cm., d.2cm.
    mid 1600s
    Strickler Site
    Lancaster County, Pennsylvania
    LA 3/517
    Lent by the State Museum of
        Pennsylvania

97. Green Goblet Base
    glass
    mid 1600s
    Strickler Site
    Lancaster County, Pennsylvania
    LA 3/517
    Lent by the State Museum of
        Pennsylvania

106

88

108, 109

98. String of Black Seed Beads
    glass
    average 1..5cm.
    early 1600s
    Washington Boro Site
    Lancaster County, Pennsylvania
    B 299
    Lent by the State Museum of
       Pennsylvania

99. String of Pale Green and White Seed
    Beads
    glass
    average 1..3cm.
    early 1600s
    Washington Boro Site
    Lancaster County, Pennsylvania
    B 290
    Lent by the State Museum of
       Pennsylvania

100. String of Blue and Black Seed Beads
     glass
     average 1..4cm.
     early 1600s
     Washington Boro Site
     Lancaster County, Pennsylvania
     B 302
     Lent by the State Museum of
        Pennsylvania

101. String of Washington Boro Blue Beads
     glass
     average 1..9cm.
     mid 1600s
     Susquehanna Valley, Pennsylvania
     uncat.
     Lent by the State Museum of
        Pennsylvania

102. String of Black and White Beads
     glass
     average d..5cm.
     17th century
     Monmouth County, New Jersey
     NJSM 80417

103. String of Black, Red and White Beads
     glass
     average d..5cm.
     17th century
     Monmouth County, New Jersey
     NJSM 80428

41

BRASS AS A RAW MATERIAL
FOR NATIVE AMERICAN CREATIVITY

...a kind of people of brownish color, quick, skillful in working with their hands, willing, clever and ready to learn and grasp a thing.

Per Lindestrom, 1654-1656

A popular trade item was the brass kettle, sturdier than the Indians' clay cooking pot. However, the kettles were not of high quality and quickly developed cracks making them useless for their original purpose. The remnants provided the Native Americans with a workable raw material. Indian groups of eastern North America had a thousands-year-old tradition of cold hammering native copper. This technology worked well with the brass kettle remnants, which were soft enough to be cut, hammered and rolled into new objects. Pendants, beads and tinklers were popular ornaments produced in this manner. Brass was also shaped into awls, formerly made of bone.

104. Washington Boro Incised Effigy Pot
clay
w.10.5cm.,h.10cm.,d.9.5cm.
17th century
Susquehanna Valley, Pennsylvania
Susquehannock Indians
B. 66
Lent by the State Museum of
Pennsylvania

105. Large Kettle
brass
h.13.5cm., d.23.5cm.
mid 1600s
Strickler Site
Lancaster County, Pennsylvania
LA 3/27
Lent by the State Museum of
Pennsylvania

106. Small Kettle
brass
h. 6.5cm., d. 7.5cm.
1575-1600
Funk/Schultz Site
Lancaster County, Pennsylvania
LA 9/184
Lent by the State Museum of
Pennsylvania

107. Necklaces with Pendants (2)
copper
1.45cm.
17th century
Camden County, New Jersey

Delaware Indians
NJSM 5340

108. Triangular Arrowpoints (3)
brass
mid 1600s
Strickler Site
Susquehannock Indians
Lancaster County, Pennsylvania
LA 3/472 b
Lent by the State Museum of
Pennsylvania

109. Hafted Brass Arrowpoint
brass, wood
l.5cm.,w.1.5cm.
1645-1665
Strickler Site
Lancaster County, Pennsylvania
Susquehannock Indians
LA 3/437
Lent by the State Museum of
Pennsylvania

It is rare to have part of the wooden
arrow shaft preserved

110. Tinkler
brass
h.5cm., w.l.9cm., d..7cm.
17th century
New Jersey
Delaware Indians
NJSM 66.727

SETTING FOR
A COLONIAL VENTURE

They set sail from

Gothenburg...laden with people,

provisions, ammunition, and

merchandise suitable for traffic

and gifts to the Indians.

Israel Acrelius, 1759

By 1638 when the two Swedish ships *Kalmar Nyckel* and *Fogel Grip* approached the Delaware River to begin the New Sweden Colony, they were not coming to a wilderness. The Dutch had been exploring the navigable portion of the river up to the Falls at Trenton for twenty years. The Indians had become used to the trade goods the Dutch and English brought to exchange for furs. The competition among the Susquehannock and the Delaware Indians for the traders' goods had led to conflict severe enough to force the Delaware Indians to abandon the western side of the river. They retreated up along the streams on the eastern bank to seek refuge from Susquehannock attacks. The Swedish colonists came to the Delaware River led by Dutchmen who knew the languages of the Indians and that the empty west bank of the river was available for colonial occupation.

111. Swedish Settlement At Fort Christina
     oil on canvas
     George Robert Bonfield (1802-98)
     w.99.2cm.,h.71cm. (framed)
     Acc. 1413
     Lent by the Philadelphia Maritime
     Museum

Goteborg, Sweden, the city from which Swedish ships bound for the colony sailed from a drawing by Erik Dahlberg
Courtesy of the Nationalmuseum, Stockholm

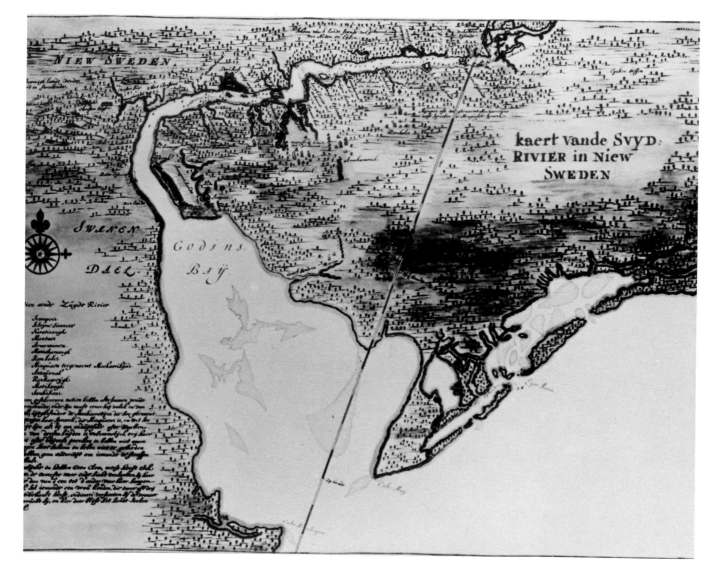

Map of the New Sweden Colony by J.
Vingboons, ca. 1640
Courtesy of the Kungliga Biblioteket, Stockholm

44

THE NEW SWEDEN COLONY
1638-1655

Swedish, Dutch and German stockholders formed the New Sweden Company to trade for furs with the Indians and to grow tobacco in North America. The Delaware River Valley was chosen as the site for the New Sweden Colony because Peter Minuit and the Dutch stockholders knew the area was well suited for both trade and tobacco growing. Minuit also knew that the Dutch and English colonies of the Atlantic seaboard were not strong enough to enforce their prior claims to the Delaware.

The Swedes landed at what is today Wilmington, Delaware, in March 1638, and began the first permanent European settlement in the Delaware Valley. Wars in Europe and economic problems at home kept Sweden from supporting the colony adequately. In the succeeding 17 years only 11 expeditions sailed from Sweden to the colony, which by 1655 consisted of scattered farms and small settlements of Swedes and Finns along both banks of the Delaware River. The colonists survived the lack of support from their homeland by pursuing a vigorous trade with the Dutch and English colonies from New England to Virginia. Conflict with the Dutch in New Amsterdam increased during the late 1640s and early 1650s. New Sweden came to an end as a Swedish colony when Governor Johan Rising surrendered to the Dutch in 1655.

THE NEW SWEDEN COLONY BEGINS

The first abode of the newly

arrived emigrants was at a place

called by the Indians

Hopakahacking. There, in the year

1638, Peter Menuit built a fortress,

which he named Fort Christina...

Israel Acrelius, 1759

The first landing of the New Sweden colonists in March 1638 was at what is today Wilmington, Delaware. There, Peter Minuit claimed the valley for Sweden and began to build Fort Christina, named for Sweden's 12-year-old Queen. Minuit bought land on the west bank of the Delaware from the Susquehannock and Delaware Indians and traded with them for furs. In the spring, he sailed for Europe but was lost at sea in a Caribbean storm. His ship returned safely, though, bringing Sweden word of the colony's start.

The Dutch protested the Swedish settlement, but they were too often at war with the Indians of northern New Jersey and southern New York and Connecticut to be able to evict the newcomers. Friction between the Dutch and the Swedes would continue for the next 17 years.

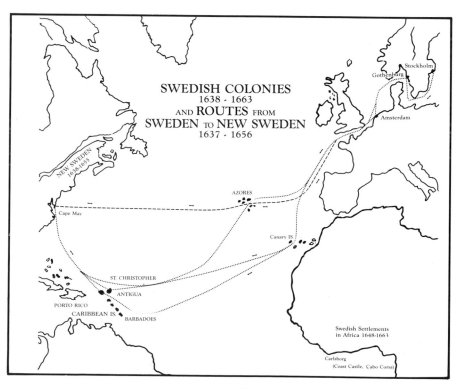

Routes across the Atlantic Ocean of Swedish expeditions
Courtesy of the Swedish Colonial Society

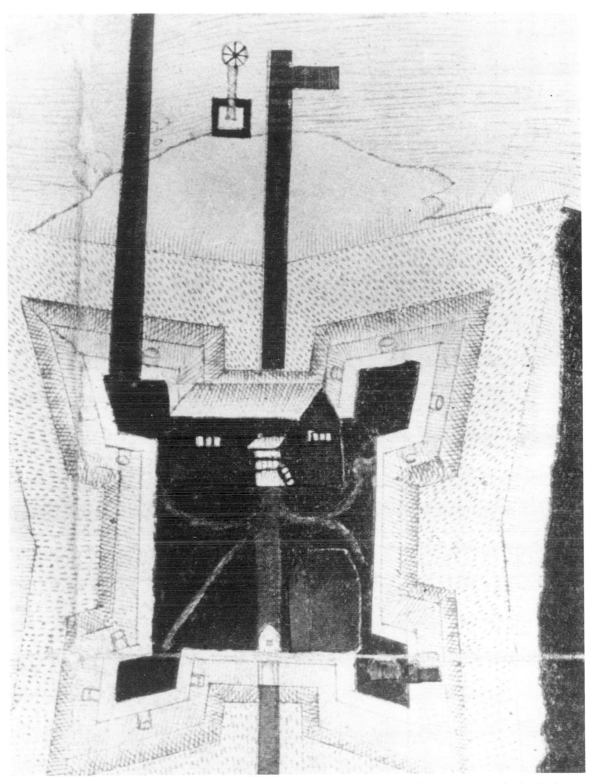

Fort Christina as drawn by Per Lindestrom
ca. 1655
Courtesy of the Riksarkivet, Stockholm

THE FIRST COLONISTS
FARMERS, SOLDIERS AND TRADERS

...accompanied by the firing of

canon...the country was called New

Sweden.

Four men from the Key of

Kalmar, 1639

The main purpose of the colony was to produce income for the investors. This is shown clearly by the composition of the first settlement. Soldiers accompanied the colonists to defend them from the Dutch and the English, who protested that they had already claimed the Delaware Valley, and the Indians. Farmers were to produce tobacco for shipment home to Sweden and to grow food for the colony. Traders were to exchange metal hoes, knives, axes and other products for furs.

Like most other colonies, New Sweden failed to produce a profit for its investors. But the colonists rarely received supplies of trade goods from Sweden. They were unable to compete successfully with the Dutch and the English for the Indian fur trade. Sweden was not overpopulated and there was no pressure for the Swedes and Finns to emigrate. The government sometimes forced those guilty of minor crimes to go to the colony. Finns living in central Sweden were sometimes sent to the colony for clearing forests which the Swedes protected for their iron and copper industries.

112. Flintlock Firearm
    iron, wood
    l. 138cm., w. 13cm., d. 7cm.
    17th century
    Falkenberg, Halland, Sweden
    73.575 b
    Lent by the Nordiska Museet,
    Stockholm

113. Finnish Plow
    wood, iron
    l.134cm., h.101cm.
    17th-century style
    Ljusnonsberg parish, Vastmanland
    Sweden
    97.266
    Lent by the Nordiska Museet,
    Stockholm

114. Large Hoe
    iron
    l.19cm., w.15.5cm., d.6cm.
    mid 1600s
    Strickler Site
    Lancaster County, Pennsylvania
    LA 3/518
    Lent by the State Museum of
    Pennsylvania

115. Large Ax Head
    iron
    l.18cm., w.10.5cm., d.3.5cm.
    early 1600s
    Susquehanna Valley, Pennsylvania
    B. 721
    Lent by the State Museum of
    Pennsylvania

116. Knife
    bone, iron
    l. 10.3cm.
    mid 1600s
    Strickler Site
    Lancaster County, Pennsylvania
    LA 3/119
    Lent by the State Museum of
    Pennsylvania

117. Crooked Knife
    iron
    w.l.5cm., d.15cm.
    17th century
    Susquehanna Valley, Pennsylvania
    Morgan Hebbard Collection
    Lent by the State Museum of
    Pennsylvania

118

JOHAN PRINTZ
FIGHT FOR SURVIVAL

He was named Captain Prins, and

a man of brave size, who weighed

over four hundred pounds.

David DeVries, 1643

Johan Printz (1592-1663) arrived in New Sweden as governor in 1643. An ex-soldier, Printz sought to strengthen the colony during his ten years of rule. He moved its headquarters from Fort Christina to Tinicum Island, which is today a part of Philadelphia. The house he built there—Printzhof—remained in his family until the 1680s.

Printz tried to centralize the colony's government. This frequently made him unpopular with his own colonists, but it earned him the respect of the surrounding Dutch and English. He forced the small group of English from New Haven, who had settled near present Salem, New Jersey, in 1641 or 1642, to swear allegiance to Sweden. He built Fort New Elfsborg near Salem to control access by the Dutch and the English to the Delaware. Throughout his service as governor Printz wrote to the government officials in Sweden asking for soldiers, artisans, settlers and trade goods. His requests went unanswered.

In 1653, despairing of help for the colony from Sweden, Printz traveled to New Amsterdam and set sail for Europe on a Dutch ship.

118. Portraits of Governor Printz'
　　Daughters (2)
　　oil on canvas
　　w.75.7cm., h.105.5cm.
　　17th century
　　anonymous artist
　　64.76.1, 64.76.2
　　Lent by the State Museum of
　　Pennsylvania

119. Piece of Fireplace Frame with Coat
　　of Arms of Governor Printz
　　sandstone
　　w.20cm., h.22cm., d.6cm.
　　ca. 1660
　　Gunillaberg, Bottnaryd, Jonkoping
　　County, Sweden
　　Lent by Mr. Bo Erhner, Jonkoping

120. Brick From Printzhof
　　clay
　　l.17.2cm., w.8cm., d.3.5cm.
　　17th century
　　Sweden or Holland
　　36DE3
　　Lent by the State Museum of
　　Pennsylvania

Printzhof is the name of the house built by Johan Printz at what is now Philadelphia as the governor's residence for the New Sweden Colony

121. Two-Handled Bowl
　　glazed, decorated red earthenware
　　h.llcm., d.31cm.
　　17th century
　　Found in excavation of old city of
　　Jonkoping
　　Lent by the Jonkoping Lans Museum,
　　Jonkoping

122. Two-Handled Bowl
　　glazed red earthenware
　　h.7.4cm., d.15.8cm.
　　mid 1600s
　　Strickler Site
　　Lancaster County, Pennsylvania
　　LA 3/588
　　Lent by the State Museum of
　　Pennsylvania

Johan Printz, governor of New Sweden from 1643 through 1653 as painted by an anonymous artist
Courtesy of the Jonkoping Lans Museum, Jonkoping

121

122

123. Cup
     glazed red earthenware
     h.5cm., d.5cm.
     17th century
     Found in excavation of old city of
        Jonkoping
     Lent by the Jonkoping Lans Museum,
        Jonkoping

124. Stove Plate
     glazed clay
     w.17cm., h.25cm.
     17th century
     Found in excavation of old city of
        Jonkoping
     Lent by the Jonkoping Lans Museum,
        Jonkoping
     Decorated with religious figures

125. Tap
     bronze
     l.15cm.
     ca. 1600

Found in excavation of old city of
   Jonkoping
Lent by the Jonkoping Lans Museum,
   Jonkoping

126. Pipe
     white clay
     l.20cm.
     17th century
     Possibly made in Holland
     Found in excavation of old city of
        Jonkoping
     Lent by the Jonkoping Lans Museum,
        Jonkoping

127. Account Book of the New Sweden
        Company
     ink, paper
     w.23.5cm., h.38.5cm., d.2cm.
     1655
     Stockholm
     Lent by the Riksarkivet, Stockholm

WAMPUM
MEDIUM FOR EXCHANGE

Wampum (called sewant by the Dutch and the Swedes) was a variety of small shell beads. It was a valuable medium of exchange between Europeans and Indians as early as the 1620s. It was also exchanged among the Indians and, until the 1640s, served as a form of "money" among the European colonists who had difficulty securing European coins.

The manufacture of wampum was time-consuming and difficult. White beads were made from the central column of a whelk shell that had been trimmed, ground smooth on gritty stones, drilled lengthwise, and finally sliced into a number of separate beads. The Indians of coastal New York and southern New England frequently made wampum with small iron drills they received from Europeans. "Black" or purple wampum was made from sections of the purple lining of a hard-shell clam. The shells were ground to a smooth cylindrical shape on gritty stones, then drilled lengthwise.

A number of white beads could be made from a single whelk column, but only a few "black" beads could be made from the small area of purple on a clam shell. Consequently, purple wampum was worth at least twice as much as white wampum.

Peter Minuit was directed on the first voyage to try to secure wampum before landing in the Delaware Valley. But Minuit took the Caribbean route rather than that by way of New England, where wampum could have been secured easily.

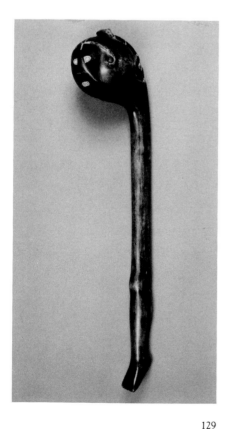

129

128. Tomahawk
    wood, iron, shell, leather, hair
    l. 49.5cm., w. 30cm., d. 2.5cm.
    17th century
    Delaware or Susquehannock Indians
    Livrustkammaren 3932
    Lent by the Etnografiska Museet,
      Stockholm

129. Ball-Headed Club
    wood, shell
    l.64cm., h.18cm., d.12cm.
    early 1600s
    Delaware or Susquehannock
    Indians
    Livrustkammaren 1010
    Lent by the Etnografiska Museet,
      Stockholm

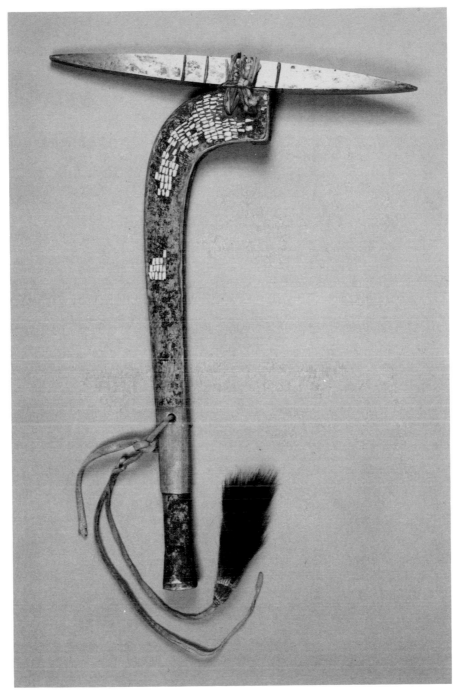

128

PEACE WITH THE INDIANS

...no Christian nation is in better

credit with the savages than we

now are.

Johan Rising, 1654

New Sweden differs from all other European colonies on the Atlantic coast of North America in one important respect—in all of its 17-year history it was never at war with the Indians. Although leaders of the colony such as Johan Printz and Johan Rising had a poor opinion of the Delaware Indians once the fur trade in the valley had been exhausted, the Swedish and Finnish settlers seem to have gotten along well with both the Delaware and the Susquehannock Indians. One reason for this is probably that the Swedes and Finns never numbered more than a few hundred settlers and therefore did not threaten to overwhelm the Indian populations.

The settlers made small clearings in the woods, burning the forest to clear trees and add fertilzer to the soil, much as the Indians themselves did. This left the settlers and the Indians free to hunt in the woods between farms. The settlers were used to hunting with the crossbow and to fishing with nets, spears and traps in the rivers. These patterns resembled the ways the Indians made their living.

130. Wolfhead Headdress
     wolf's skull with teeth intact, hide, shell, sinew, with fur dyed red
     1.84cm., w.14cm., h.9.5cm.
     17th century
     Delaware or Susquehannock Indians
     6912
     Lent by Skoklosters slott, Balsta

131. Ball-Headed Club
     wood, brass
     1.40cm., d.9.5cm.
     17th century
     Delaware or Susquehannock Indians
     6906
     Lent by Skoklosters slott, Balsta

132. Linked Fur-Covered Cords
     hide, fur, sinew, twined fiber and blue trade cloth
     l.75cm., w.30.5cm., d.l.3cm.
     17th century
     Delaware or Susquehannock Indians
     6910
     Lent by Skoklosters slott, Balsta

133. Burden Strap
     twined fiber
     l.560cm., w.4.7cm.
     17th century
     Delaware or Susquehannock Indians
     6908
     Lent by Skoklosters slott, Balsta

     The burden strap was worn by Indian women around their foreheads to support heavy loads on their backs.

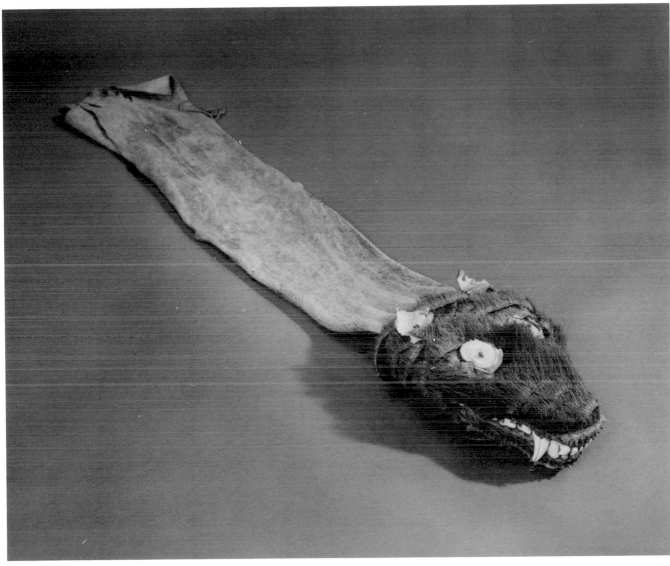

130

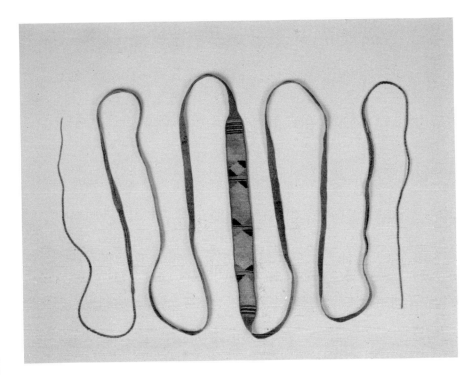

131

A BRIEF WAR—AND
THE END OF A COLONY

...the Dutch...brought the guns of

all their batteries to bear upon us,

and on the 14th instant, formally

summoned Fort Christina, with

harsh menaces, by a drummer and

a messenger, to capitulate within

twenty-four hours.

Johan Rising, 1655

The Dutch-Swedish rivalry for control of the Delaware Valley was intense. The Swedish settlement was a commercial and potentially a military threat to New Netherland. Perhaps the Dutch tolerated the Swedes on their flank because New Netherland's relations with the neighboring Indians were poor at best, and often degenerated into open warfare. Another reason may have been that the generally cordial relations in Europe among England, the Netherlands and Sweden extended to a measure of mutual tolerance among their colonies in the New World.

But in 1654 Printz was succeeded as governor by the somewhat less judicious Johan Rising, when New Netherland was governed by the energetic Peter Stuyvesant. Soon after he arrived in the New World, Rising attempted to dislodge the Dutch from the valley by seizing Fort Casimir (present New Castle, Delaware), below Fort Christina on the western shore of the river. Stuyvesant responded by attacking New Sweden late in the summer of 1655. The virtually bloodless Dutch conquest ended Swedish sovereignty—though not the Swedish and Finnish presence—in the Delaware Valley.

134. Novi Belgii, Novaeque Angliae
     engraving, color
     w.55.6cm., h.46.7cm.
     Nikolaus J. Visscher
     ca. 1656
     Holland
     Lent by the New Jersey State Archives

135. Charles II Medallion
     silver
     h.3.6cm., w.2.8cm.
     post 1660
     Strickler Site
     Lancaster County, Pennsylvania
     LA 3/450 a
     Lent by the State Museum of
        Pennsylvania

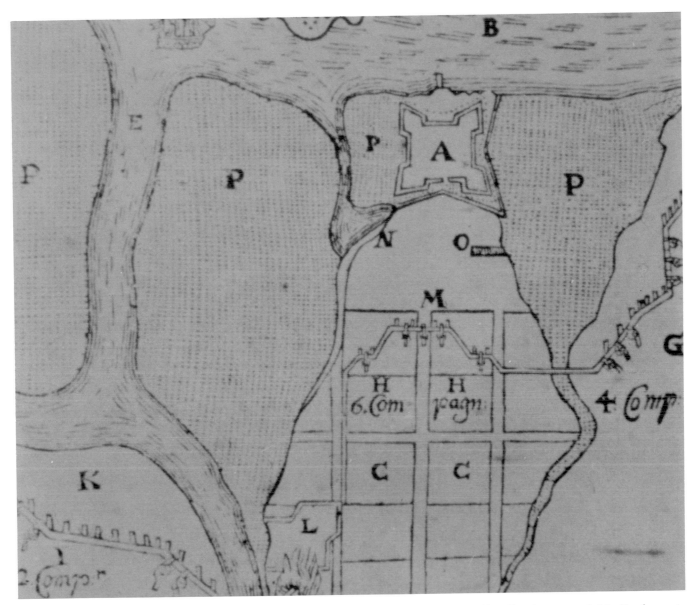

Fort Christina surrounded by Dutch guns in
1655 as drawn by Per Lindestrom
Courtesy of the Riksarkivet, Stockholm

Hunting and fishing in 17th- century
Scandinavia as drawn by Erik Dahlberg
Courtesy of the Nationalmuseum, Stockholm

60

SELF-SUFFICIENT SWEDES AND FINNS

While the New Sweden colony was a political and economic failure, the settlers made a successful adaptation to life in the Delaware Valley.

The Swedish and Finnish colonists probably made the transition from the Old World to the new more successfully than any other group of European settlers. This resulted from similarities of natural environment between northeastern North America and Sweden-Finland, and similarities in the lifestyles of the colonists and the Indians which minimized conflict between the two peoples.

New Sweden fell, but the Scandinavian presence on the Delaware River remained. Swedish and Finnish contributions to the culture of colonial North America remained important throughout the 18th century and are significant in the modern United States (enhanced by later, heavier Swedish and Finnish immigration from the 1840s to the 1920s).

These influences include foodways, local place names, music, church organization, log architecture, domestic weaving, Appalachian dulcimers, several boat types, and a number of cast iron objects. New Sweden also influenced culture at higher levels through the paintings of Gustav Hesselius, published and unpublished poetry and hymns, and histories and descriptions of North America by Swedish and Finnish visitors such as Pehr Kalm, Per Lindestrom, Israel Acrelius, and Nils Collin.

THE FIRST AMERICAN PIONEERS

...a plain, strong, industrious

people,.

William Penn, 1683

The Swedes and the Finns who came to the Delaware as colonists were probably better prepared to deal with the New World's climates and landforms than any other European settlers. Sweden was similar physically in many ways to North America. The techniques developed in Sweden over past centuries to extract a living from such an environment served them as well in the Delaware River Valley. The lifestyle they brought with them was also similar to that of the Indians.

Like the Native Americans, the Swedes and the Finns were used to supporting themselves through a combination of farming, hunting and fishing. They lived in self-sufficient households, where men built their own log houses and outbuildings, made their farming and hunting tools and much of the household equipment, such as furniture and bowls. The women spun, wove and sewed the clothing for their families and their household "linens."

136. Chest
   wood, iron
   l.134.5cm., w.56cm., h.52cm.
   1621
   Sweden
   161.840
   Lent by the Nordiska Museet,
     Stockholm

137. Plow
   wood, iron
   l.123cm., h.89cm.
   17th-century style
   Sweden
   79.319
   Lent by the Nordiska Museet,
     Stockholm

138. Door From a Peasant Storehouse
   pinewood, iron
   w. 129cm., h. 188cm.
   17th century (?)
   Mora parish, Dalarna,
     Sweden
   85.585a-c
   Lent by the Nordiska Museet,
     Stockholm

139. Forge Hammer
   iron, wood
   l.36cm., w.14.5cm.
   17th-century style
   Sweden
   144.552
   Lent by the Nordiska Museet,
     Stockholm

140. Forge Tongs
   forged iron
   l.61.5cm., w.20cm.
   17th-century style
   farmer's forge, Drangsered parish,
     Halland, Sweden
   91.394e
   Lent by the Nordiska Museet,
     Stockholm

141. Brickmaker's Mold
   pinewood
   l. 36.2cm., w. 22cm.
   17th-century style
   Ranea parish, Norrbottan, Sweden
   171.670
   Lent by the Nordiska Museet,
     Stockholm

136

142. Cloth Used by Beaters in Communal
     Hunts (6)
     paint on canvas, rope
     average l. 50cm., w. 50cm.
     17th century (?)
     Sweden
     T 281a-f
     Lent by the Nordiska Museet,
     Stockholm

143. Hunting Spear
     iron, wood, brass
     17th-century style
     Sweden
     303.118
     Lent by the Nordiska Museet,
     Stockholm

144. Crossbow
     wood, iron,
     l.98cm., w.66cm.
     17th-century style
     Sweden
     29.691
     Lent by the Nordiska Museet,
     Stockholm

145. Fishing Spear
     wood, iron
     l.297cm., w.11.5cm.
     17th-century style
     Lycksele lappmark, Lappland
     114.189
     Lent by the Nordiska Museet,
     Stockholm

146. Fish Trap
     wood, birchbark
     l.105cm., d.35cm.
     17th-century style
     Sweden
     149.559
     Lent by the Nordiska Museet,
     Stockholm

147. Netsinker
     stone, birchbark
     17th-century style
     Sweden
     227.753
     Lent by the Nordiska Museet,
     Stockholm

146

148. Butter Churn
    wood
    h.100cm.
    marked IES 1640
    Borgsjo parish, Jamtland, Sweden
    45.599
    Lent by the Nordiska Museet,
      Stockholm

149. Plate
    wood
    d.19cm.
    Probably 18th century
    Jonkoping County, Sweden
    Lent by the Jonkoping Lans Museum,
      Jonkoping

150. Spoon
    horn
    l.15cm., w.8cm.
    17th-century style
    Sweden
    160.274
    Lent by the Nordiska Museet,
      Stockholm

151. Spoon
    wood
    l.14.5cm., w.7.5cm.
    17th-century style
    Vackelsang parish, Smaland, Sweden
    63.090a
    Lent by the Nordiska Museet,
      Stockholm

152. Dragonfly
    wood
    l.48cm., d.6.5cm.
    17th-century style
    Sarna parish, Dalarna, Sweden
    26.805 a
    Lent by the Nordiska Museet,
      Stockholm

153. Needle Box
    elk horn
    l. 10cm.
    dated 1641
    Transtrond parish, Dalarna, Sweden
    30.677
    Lent by the Nordiska Museet,
      Stockholm

THE LUTHERAN CHURCH
TIES WITH OLD SWEDEN

...I have caused a church to be built in New Gothenburg, decorating it according to our Swedish fashion, so far as our resources and means would allow.

Johan Printz, 1647

Long after the end of the New Sweden colony in 1655, the Swedish and Finnish settlers in the Delaware Valley tried to maintain cultural ties with Sweden. In 1693, feeling lost, perhaps, in the Englishness of their surroundings, they petitioned King Karl XI to send them priests, catechisms and hymnals to help them keep alive their Lutheran faith and their Swedish language. Thereafter ministers from Sweden helped to maintain the settlers' ties with the old country until the American Revolution.

The role of the Swedish Lutheran Church in maintaining this tie was both formal and very important. Beginning early in the 18th century, Jasper Swedberg, the Bishop of Skara in western Sweden, was given charge of the mission to the New World. He and his successors sent over such Lutheran priests as Andreas Hesselius, Erik Bjork, Israel Acrelius and Nils Collin.

Their parsonages were a network of cultural continuity for visitors from home. For example, when in the late 1740s and early 1750s, the Finnish naturalist Pehr Kalm traveled through the Delaware Valley, he stayed at Lutheran parsonages such as the one at Swedesboro, New Jersey.

The reports and letters home of Lutheran divines such as Erik Bjork contain early descriptions of the region, the lives of the Swedes and the Finns in the river, and the culture of the English colonies in which they lived. Later published accounts by Israel Acrelius and Nils Collin echo Bjork's observations.

The Lutheran missionaries to New Sweden not only succored their coreligionists, they also tried to bring the Christian message to the Indians. In 1696 the Swedish government printed Thomas Campanius's translation of Martin Luther's catechism into the Delaware Indian language, and the first ministers of the Swedish Mission in America brought copies with them to the Delaware Valley.

Skara, seat of the Lutheran Bishops who sent ministers to the Delaware Valley in the 18th Century as drawn by Erik Dahlberg
Courtesy of the Nationalmuseum, Stockholm

156

154. Johannes Campanius' Translation of Martin Luther's Catechism Into the Delaware Indian Language
ink, paper, leather
w.10.5cm., h.6.5cm., d.1cm.
1696
Stockholm
Lent by Special Collections and Archives, Rutgers University Libraries

155. Thomas Campanius Holm's *Description of the Province of New Sweden*
ink, paper, leather
1702
Stockholm
Lent by Rare Book Collections, Firestone Library, Princeton University

156. Priest's Altar Service Robe
Red velvet with embroidered gilt and silver thread
w.88cm., h.121cm.
1761

Church of Aker, Jonkoping County, Sweden
Lent by the Jonkoping Lans Museum, Jonkoping

157. Israel Acrelius' Account of the Swedish Churches in New Sweden
ink, paper
1759
Stockholm
Lent by Rare Book Collections, Firestone Library, Princeton University

158. Pehr Kalm's *Travels in North America*
ink, paper
w.22cm., h.28cm., d.5.5cm.
Dutch edition of 1772
Utrecht, Holland
Lent by Special Collections and Archives, Rutgers University Libraries

CULTURAL INFLUENCES

Several old men in this country told me that the Swedes on their arrival here made such fences as are usual in Sweden, but they were forced to leave off in a few years time, because they could not get posts enough.

Pehr Kalm, 1749

The influences of New Sweden go deep into American material culture.

The colonists are usually credited with bringing to North America such common Americanisms as log architecture, post-and-rail fences and the sauna. But there are numerous other ways in which they may have influenced the manner in which Americans have lived over the past three and a half centuries.

Some folklife scholars theorize that the Swedes and the Finns may have learned from the Indians to make canoes. But the colonists were used to traveling the waterways of Sweden-Finland in church boats, and they may have been familiar with the technology of the dugout from building these boats. The church boats may, in fact, have been the ancestors of the famous Durham boats in which the Continental army crossed the Delaware to attack the Hessians at Trenton on Christmas night, 1776.

Other Swedish crafts may have influenced colonial American technologies. Swedish iron working may have influenced early Pennsylvania iron working techniques, and the weaving styles of Swedish and Finnish women seem to have contributed to the middle Atlantic tradition of woven coverlets.

There is even a tradition that the Swedish and Finnish style of living in a forested environment, a style that conserved at least as much as it used, was the basis of the forestry industry of southern New Jersey.

The settlers may also have influenced Indian crafts and technologies, other than through the obvious mechanism of trading metal implements for furs. For example, by the early years of the 19th century the Delaware Indians were producing beautiful splint baskets to sell to European-Americans, and they seem to have taught the technique to other Indians of the eastern seaboard. But this technology is originally Swedish and Finnish, and the Delaware may have learned it from the settlers. And east-coast Indian storehouses, from New England to the middle Atlantic, resemble nothing so much as the traditional Finnish style of storehouse.

159. Knapsack
birchbark
17th-century style
Sweden
88.781
Lent by the Nordiska Museet,
Stockholm

160. Basket
wood
l.46cm., h.33.5cm.
19th or early 20th century
Northeastern United States
Possibly Mohegan Indians
NJSM 3261

The practice of making woven
splint baskets spread from the
Delaware Indians to other Native
Americans in the eastern United
States.

161. Basket
dye, wood
l.32cm., w.24cm., h.14cm.
19th or early 20th century
Burlington County, New Jersey
Delaware Indians
NJSM 66.343

162. Basket
paint, dye, wood
l.32cm., w.26cm., h.14.5cm.
19th or early 20th century
Burlington County, New Jersey
Delaware Indians
NJSM 66.336

It has been suggested that the
Delaware Indians may have
learned to make woven splint
baskets from the Swedish and
Finnish settlers in the Delaware
Valley.

163. Dugout Canoe
white cedar
l.335.3cm.
17th century
Cape May County, New Jersey
NJSM

Hollowed out by burning and
scraping, dugout canoes were used
by the Indians of the Delaware
Valley and according to Pehr
Kalm by Swedish settlers in the
1750s.

Swedesboro, New Jersey (called Raccoon by
the Swedish settlers) in the 1840s
J.W. Barber and Henry Howe, *Historical
Collections of the State of New Jersey* (1844)

BIBLIOGRAPHY

Acrelius, Israel
   1874 *A History of New Sweden: or, The Settlements on the
   Delaware River.* Philadelphia: Historical Society of Pennsylvania.

Andersson, Ingvar
   1956 *A History of Sweden.* New York: Praeger.

Clay, Jehu Curtis
   1858 *Annals of the Swedes on the Delaware, From Their First Settlement in 1636, To
   the Present Time.* Philadelphia:
   H. Hooker & Co.

Collin, Nicholas
   1936 *The Journal and Biography of Nicholas Collin.*
   Philadelphia: The New Jersey Society of Pennsylvania.

Federal Writers' Project, New Jersey
   1938 *The Swedes and Finns in New Jersey.* The New Jersey Commission to
   Commemorate the 300th Anniversary of the Settlement by the Swedes and
   Finns on the Delaware.

Goddard, Ives
   1978 Delaware, *Handbook of North American Indians Northeast* Vol. 15.
   Washington, D.C.: Smithsonian Institution.

Holm, Thomas Campanius
   1702 *A Brief Description of the Province of New Sweden, Now Called by the English,
   Pennsylvania, in America. Compiled from the Relations and Writings of Persons
   Worthy of Credit, and Adorned with Maps and Plates.*
   Stockholm.

Jameson, J. F. (Ed.)
   1909 *Narratives of New Netherland, 1609-1664.* New York:
   Charles Scribner's Sons.

Johnson, Amandus
   1911 *The Swedish Settlements on the Delaware: Their History and Relation to the
   Indians, Dutch and English, 1638-1664.* 2 Vols. Philadelphia: University of
   Pennsylvania Press.
   1927 *The Swedes on the Delaware, 1638-1664.* Philadelphia.
   1930 *The Instruction for Johan Printz, Governor of New Sweden.* Philadelphia:
   Swedish Colonial Society.

Kalm, Peter
   1987 *Peter Kalm's Travels in North America, The English Version of 1770.* New
   York: Dover Publications.

Kent, Barry C.
   1984 *Susquehanna's Indians.* Harrisburg, Pa.: Pennsylvania Historical and Museum
   Commission.

Kraft, Herbert C.
1986 *The Lenape: Archaeology, History, and Ethnography.*
Newark, N.J.: New Jersey Historical Society.

Leiby, Adrian C.
1964 *The Early Dutch and Swedish Settlers of New Jersey.*
Princeton, N.J.: Van Nostrand.

Lindestrom, Peter
1925 *Geographia Americae, With an Account of the Delaware Indians, Based on Surveys and Notes Made in 1654-1656.*
Philadelphia: Swedish Colonial Society.

Myers, Albert Cook (Ed.)
1912 *Narratives of Early Pennsylvania, West New Jersey and Delaware, 1630-1707.*
New York: Charles Scribner's Sons.

Rink, Oliver A.
1986 *Holland on the Hudson: An Economic and Social History of Dutch New York.*
Ithaca, N.Y.: Cornell University Press.

Roberts, Michael
1968 *The Swedish Imperial Experience, 1560-1718.* New York:
Cambridge University Press.

Scott, Franklin D.
1977 *Sweden: The Nation's History.* Minneapolis: University of Minnesota Press.

Wacker, Peter O.
1975 *Land and People: A Cultural Geography of Preindustrial New Jersey: Origins and Settlement Patterns.* New Brunswick, N.J.: Rutgers University Press.

Ward, Christopher
1930 *The Dutch and Swedes on the Delaware, 1609-64.*
Philadelphia: University of Pennsylvania Press.
1938 New Sweden on the Delaware. Philadelphia: University of Pennsylvania Press.

Weslager, C. A.
1961 *Dutch Explorers, Traders and Settlers in the Delaware Valley, 1609-1664* (in collaboration with A.R. Dunlap).
Philadelphia: University of Pennsylvania Press.
1967 *The English on the Delaware, 1610-1682.* New Brunswick, N.J.: Rutgers University Press.
1987 *The Swedes and Dutch at New Castle.* Wilmington: Middle Atlantic Press of Delaware.
1988 *New Sweden on the Delaware, 1638-1655.* Wilmington: Middle Atlantic Press.

Wuorinen, John H.
1938 *The Finns on the Delaware, 1638-1655: An Essay in American Colonial History.*
New York: Columbia University Press.